HEAR AMERICA SINGING

Let music swell the breeze,
And ring from all the trees
Sweet freedom's song;
Let mortal tongues awake,
Let all that breathe partake;
Let rocks their silence break,
The sound prolong.

"America"
Reverend Samuel E. Smith

IDEALS PUBLISHING CORPORATION
NASHVILLE, TENNESSEE

Publisher, Patricia A. Pingry; Book Editor, Nancy J. Skarmeas;
Art Director, Patrick T. McRae; Copy Editor, Donna Sigalos Budjenska
Book Design and Artwork by Stacy Venturi-Pickett

ISBN 0-8249-1117-2

ACKNOWLEDGMENTS

"Semper Paratus." Words and music by Captain F. S. Van Boskerck. Copyright © 1938 and 1986
by Sam Fox Publishing Company, Inc., Santa Barbara, California. All Rights Reserved. Used by
Permission.

ILLUSTRATION CREDITS

7, *Paul Revere's Ride*, Hy Hintermeister, Superstock; 11, *Cornwallis Surrenders to Washington at
Yorktown*, Hy Hintermeister, Superstock; 15, *USS Constitution Salutes the Tall Ships*, FPG; 19,
George Washington, Gilbert Stuart, Superstock; 23, Flag and fireworks, Dick Dietrich Photo; 27,
Eagle, flag, and Statue of Liberty, Superstock; 31, *Lincoln at Independence Hall*, J. L. G. Ferris,
Superstock; 35, Fireworks over Washington, D. C., Jake McGuire, Washington Stock Photo; 39,
The Wounded Drummer Boy, Eastman Johnson, Superstock; 43, Mt.. Hood overlooks summer dis-
play of lupines in Cairn Basin, Oregon, Jeff Gnass Photo; 46, John Philip Sousa, Archive Photos;
50, United States Marine Corps War Memorial, G. Silverstein, Washington Stock Photo; 54,
USS Constitution, courtesy United States Naval Academy Museum; 57, United States Military
Academy Color Guard, courtesy United States Military Academy, West Point, N.Y.; 61, United
States Coast Guard training ship *Eagle*, courtesy United States Coast Guard; 63, United States
Air Force Thunderbirds, courtesy United States Air Force Air Demonstration Squadron; 64,
Children and flag, Superstock; 69, *Betsy Ross Shows George Washington the Stars and Stripes*,
Superstock; 77, Heceta Head, Oregon, Dick Dietrich Photo.

COVER ART
FOURTH OF JULY IN AMERICA
FRANCIS CHASE

Table of Contents

FOREWORD

I hear America singing, the varied carols I hear," wrote Walt Whitman in 1855. Today, almost one hundred and fifty years later, America remains a land of great diversity. We speak in an endless variety of accents. We trace our family heritage to every country of the world. We support opposing causes and we maintain countless regional customs. Despite our differences, however, we are bound together by a common love of country; and nothing expresses this love more eloquently than song. Patriotic music melds our varied American voices into one glorious, harmonious chorus.

Patriotic songs touch a common chord in each of us. Every American can know the pride and longing felt by John Philip Sousa, who wrote the legendary march "The Stars and Stripes Forever" after experiencing a vision of Old Glory on a trip across the Atlantic toward American shores. We set our regional differences aside to share with Katharine Lee Bates the awe and reverence at the sight of the Rocky Mountains that inspired the lyrics to "America the Beautiful." And who among us is immune to the sorrow of war that moved Julia Ward Howe to write "The Battle Hymn of the Republic"?

Patriotic songs transcend our differences and remind us of what binds us together as a nation. Our common national heritage can be traced through the patriotic music we have

4

written, played, and sung. When challenges have arisen, songs have helped rally Americans to the service of great causes. In the darkest hours of national crisis and despair, songs have brought comfort and hope. Through music we have expressed our love of country and our pride in our nation's accomplishments, and we have given voice to our more humble feelings of gratitude and thanks for a multitude of blessings. Over two hundred years ago, marching toward the redcoated British regulars, a small contingent of ragtag colonial soldiers boldly sang "Yankee Doodle." Since that time, America has changed almost beyond recognition, but the pride and love of country that inspired those "Yankee" soldiers to rise up against tyranny remains strong in American hearts today.

Toward the end of the Civil War, President Abraham Lincoln gave special praise to Chicago songwriter George F. Root, author of "The Battle Cry of Freedom." The President told Root that he had served his country well, doing more with his one song to lift the morale of the troops than "a hundred generals and a thousand orators." Lincoln was merely giving formal recognition to something Americans had known since the founding of the nation, that is that music—particularly patriotic music—has a unique power to comfort, unite, and inspire.

THE LIBERTY SONG

WORDS AND MUSIC BY JOHN DICKINSON

The Liberty Song," written in 1768, stated plainly and boldly something many American colonists had quietly whispered for years: taxation of the colonists by Great Britain was unlawful and unjust.

The song's author, Philadelphia lawyer and gentleman farmer John Dickinson, had espoused the same belief the previous year in his "Farmer's Letters." These treatises were widely read by colonial leaders and scholars, but it was the musical adaptation of Dickinson's idea that sparked the interest of the farmers and common folk and helped fan the flames of revolution. Within weeks of the song's first publication, it could be heard throughout the colonies at political protest meetings, family celebrations, and anywhere else the beleaguered colonists gathered.

"The Liberty Song" told the colonists nothing they did not already know. It did, however, cross educational and social boundaries and unite Americans in one voice on a single issue that touched each of them. This simple song helped transform the once unthinkable idea of an America independent from British control into the solid foundation of a great revolution. "The Liberty Song," America's first native political song, proved early in our nation's history that music has a power beyond the written or spoken word to unite and inspire.

6

Like the stirring verses of "The Liberty Song," Hy Hintermeister's *Paul Revere's Ride* captures the drama and passion of the days leading up to the American Revolution. With his midnight cries of "The British are coming! The British are coming!" Paul Revere served notice on the colonists that the time to stand up and fight for independence was at hand.

THE LIBERTY SONG

Come join hand in hand brave A - mer - i - cans all, And rouse your bold hearts at fair Lib - er - ty's call; No ty - ran - nous acts shall sup - press your just claim, Or stain with dis - hon - our A - mer - i - ca's name.

Chorus

In Free - dom we're born and in Free - dom we'll live, Our — pur - ses are read - y, Stead - y, Friends, Stead - y, Not as Slaves, but as Free - men our mon - ey we'll give.

8

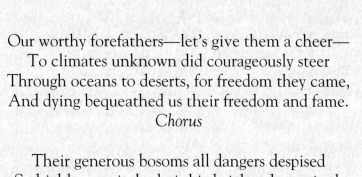

Our worthy forefathers—let's give them a cheer—
To climates unknown did courageously steer
Through oceans to deserts, for freedom they came,
And dying bequeathed us their freedom and fame.
Chorus

Their generous bosoms all dangers despised
So highly, so wisely their birthrights they prized;
We'll keep what they gave, we will piously keep,
Nor frustrate their toils on the land and the deep.
Chorus

The tree their own hands had to liberty reared
They lived to behold grow as strong and revered;
With transport they cried: "now our wishes we gain,
For our children will gather the fruits of our pain."
Chorus

Then join hand in hand brave Americans all,
By uniting we stand, by dividing we fall;
In so righteous a cause let us hope to succeed,
For heaven approves of each generous deed.
Chorus

All ages shall speak with amaze and applause,
Of the courage we'll show in support of our laws:
To die we can bear—but to serve we disdain,
For shame is to freedom more dreadful than pain.
Chorus

This bumper I crown for our Sovereign's health,
And this for Britannia's glory and wealth;
That wealth and that glory immortal may be,
If she is but just—and if we are free.
Chorus

9

YANKEE DOODLE
WORDS AND MUSIC TRADITIONAL

The American colonists entered the Revolutionary War boldly, with confidence in themselves and in their mission. Their opponents, however, regarded them as nothing more than a nuisance. The polished British Redcoats expressed their disregard in a humorous little song called "Yankee Doodle," which ridiculed the colonists (a "doodle" was a fool), their ragged dress, and their less-than-precise military maneuvers. Most of all, the song ridiculed the colonists' visions of independence.

The British, of course, underestimated the colonists on all counts. They lost the war; they lost their colonies; and they also lost their song. In the spirit of their rebellion, the American soldiers claimed "Yankee Doodle" as a rallying song of their own. As the Revolutionary War continued, the British had little time or spirit for their humorous renditions of "Yankee Doodle." They could only listen in humbled silence as their opponents proudly played and sang the song with increasing regularity.

By war's end, the transformation was complete. As British leader Cornwallis prepared to surrender his troops to General George Washington at Yorktown in October of 1781, the American fife and drum corps played "Yankee Doodle." The sneer of British contempt was now an anthem of American pride. The British had made many mistakes in the war, not the least of which had been underestimating the power of a simple song.

The proudest performance of "Yankee Doodle" was surely that of the colonial fife and drum corps at the surrender of the British troops to General George Washington at Yorktown in 1781. The surrender, depicted here by twentieth-century American artist Hy Hintermeister, marked the end of the American Revolution and the beginning of the American nation.

YANKEE DOODLE

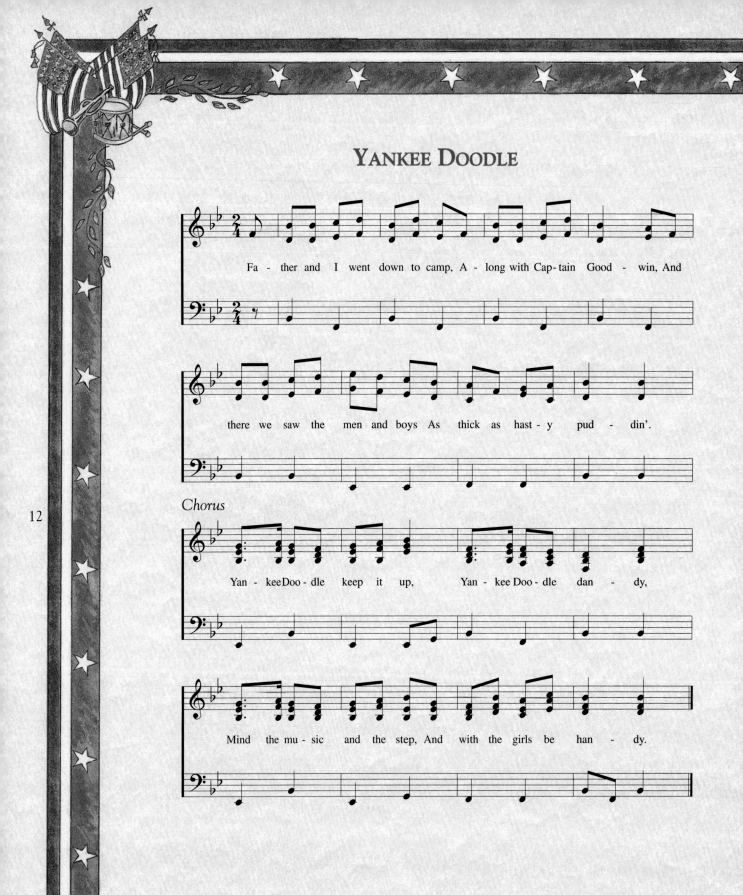

Fa - ther and I went down to camp, A - long with Cap - tain Good - win, And

there we saw the men and boys As thick as hast - y pud - din'.

Chorus

Yan - kee Doo - dle keep it up, Yan - kee Doo - dle dan - dy,

Mind the mu - sic and the step, And with the girls be han - dy.

12

And there was Captain Washington
Upon a strapping stallion,
And giving orders to his men,
I guess there was a million.
Chorus

And the feathers on his hat
They looked so tarnal finey
I wanted peskily to get
To give to my Jemimy.
Chorus

And there I see a little keg,
Its heads were made of leather;
They knocked upon it with two sticks
To call the men together.
Chorus

And there they had a swamping gun,
As big as a log of maple,
Upon a dueced little cart,
A load for father's cattle.
Chorus

And every time they fired it off
It took a horn of powder;
It made a noise like father's gun,
Only a nation louder.
Chorus

It scared me so, I ran the streets,
Nor stopped, as I remember,
Till I got home and safely locked
In Granny's little chamber.
Chorus

Hail! Columbia

Words by Joseph Hopkinson
Music from "The President's March"

Seventeen ninety-eight was a year of crisis for the young American nation. A raging conflict between England and France had so sharply divided loyalties in the United States that Americans had begun to lose sight of their own national identity and purpose. Gilbert Fox, a famous singer who was preparing for a performance at Philadelphia's New Theatre, decided that his audience needed a new patriotic song to turn their attention back to their homeland. He turned for help to his friend, lawyer, legislator, judge, and amateur songwriter, Joseph Hopkinson.

Hopkinson gave Fox a song he called "Hail! Columbia." Sung to the music of "The President's March," a familiar American tune said to have been played at the inauguration of George Washington, "Hail! Columbia" reminded Americans of the battles they had fought only a few years earlier and of the responsibilities and privileges of the independence they had secured. No mention was made of either England or France; "Hail! Columbia" was a song for America.

"Hail! Columbia" debuted at Philadelphia's New Theatre in 1798. Its opening night audience included First Lady Abigail Adams, who reported that the song inspired such thunderous and continuous applause that her "head ached in consequence of it." Thereafter, "Hail! Columbia" became the unofficial national anthem, treasured by Americans for reminding them that theirs was a nation equal to any other and deserving of their first and fiercest loyalty.

14

This beautiful painting commemorates the visit of the world's tall ships to Boston Harbor in 1976 to join in our celebration of the American Bicentennial. The majestic old Navy ship offering a salute to the visitors is the USS *Constitution*, a veteran of many battles and now a fixture in Boston Harbor, where it offers visitors from around the world a glimpse into American naval history.

John Charles Roach

HAIL! COLUMBIA

16

what it costs; Ev - er grate - ful for the prize,

Let its al - tar reach the skies. Firm, u - nit - ed,

let us be, Ral - lying round our lib - er - ty,

As a band of broth - ers joined,

Peace and safe - ty we shall find.

17

HAIL TO THE CHIEF
WORDS AND MUSIC BY JAMES SANDERSON

The years after the Revolutionary War were difficult and dangerous for Americans. They had declared themselves a sovereign nation; they had fought and died to secure that sovereignty. Thereafter they faced the greatest battle of all: transforming the idea of the United States of America into a secure nation.

How to define the presidency was one great task. Americans needed a leader, and their experiences during the colonial years had taught them they did not want a king. Exactly what type of leader did this new kind of nation want and need? The answer came slowly. The office of the presidency evolved, borrowing from European models and applying the tenets of the new nation until the presidency became the powerful and respected position it is today. The same is true of the president's song, "Hail to the Chief."

Like the office itself, the president's song evolved from British origins. It was written in 1812 by James Sanderson, who intended it as a musical setting for Sir Walter Scott's play *The Lady of the Lake*. Twenty-five years later, the song was heard by guests at the inauguration of President Van Buren. Twenty-five more years saw the song featured as a prominent part of the inauguration and the inaugural ball of President Lincoln in March 1861. And today, the opening notes of "Hail to the Chief" are a universally unmistakable prelude to the entrance of the President of the United States of America.

18

The symbols of the presidency—the White House, the Presidential Seal, and the song, "Hail to the Chief"—remind our presidents of the great leaders who have served before them. One of the greatest of these men was George Washington. Shown here in a Gilbert Stuart portrait, Washington set an example of courage and integrity that presidents have emulated for over two hundred years.

HAIL TO THE CHIEF

Hail to the Chief we have chos - en for the na - tion,

Hail to the Chief! We sa - lute him, one and all.

Hail to the Chief, as we pledge co - op - er - a - tion

In proud ful - fill - ment of a great, no - ble call.

20

Yours is the aim to make this grand coun - try grand - er,

This you will do, That's our strong, firm be - lief.

Hail to the one we se - lect - ed as com - mand - er,

Hail to the Pres - i - dent! Hail to the Chief!

21

THE STAR-SPANGLED BANNER

WORDS BY FRANCIS SCOTT KEY

MUSIC FROM BRITISH "ANACREON IN HEAVEN"

In 1814, British troops attacked Washington, D.C., setting fire to the president's mansion and other government buildings and throwing the young American nation into turmoil.

After the attack, the British retreated to Baltimore Harbor to plan their next offensive: an attack on Fort McHenry. About this time, Maryland lawyer Francis Scott Key boarded a small British cartel boat to negotiate for the release of a close friend held prisoner. The British admiral agreed to release the prisoner; but because Key had observed the preparations for the upcoming attack, he was not allowed to leave. Thus, Key spent a restless and fearful night, a captive witness to the furious British assault on American Fort McHenry.

Key saw the nation he loved tested that night. From midnight throughout the early morning hours, sixteen ships bombarded Fort McHenry. When dawn broke Key saw that, tattered but intact, "the flag was still there." Overcome with relief and pride he wrote the words that would become our national anthem.

Key's lyrics, set to the British tune "Anacreon in Heaven," quickly became an unofficial national anthem. It was not until 1931, however, that the President signed the bill granting "The Star-Spangled Banner" official status. Even then there were dissenters who argued the song was too militaristic to represent a peace-loving nation. The protests went unheeded, however, for Key's song is not about war, but about a nation with the strength and courage to withstand any challenge in defense of its shores, people, and ideals. To people across the globe, "The Star-Spangled Banner" is recognized as the anthem of freedom.

We celebrate the Fourth of July with fireworks and flag waving, a ceremonial recreation of the night Francis Scott Key spent aboard the British ship *Minden* watching "the rockets' red glare, the bombs bursting in air." The joy Key felt upon the sight of the flag at dawn is a feeling all Americans share each time they hear his song.

THE STAR-SPANGLED BANNER

1. O say, can you see, by the dawn's ear - ly
2. On the shore dim - ly seen thro' the mists of the
3. And where is the band who so vaunt - ing - ly
4. O thus be it ev - er, when free men shall

light, What so proud - ly we hail'd at the twi - light's last
deep, Where the foe's haugh - ty host in dread si - lence re -
swore, 'Mid the hav - oc of war and the bat - tle's con -
stand Be - tween their loved homes and the war's des - o -

gleam - ing? Whose broad stripes and bright stars, thro' the per - il - ous
pos - es, What is that which the breeze, o'er the tow - er - ing
fu - sion, A home and a coun - try they'd leave us no
la - tion; Blest with vict - 'ry and peace, may the heav'n res - cued

fight, O'er the ram - parts we watched, were so gal - lant - ly
steep. As it fit - ful - ly blows, half con - ceals, half dis -
more? Their blood has wash'd out their foul foot - step's pol -
land Praise the Power that hath made and pre - served us a

25

AMERICA
WORDS BY SAMUEL FRANCIS SMITH
MUSIC FROM BRITISH "GOD SAVE THE KING"

The Star Spangled Banner" is our national anthem; but "America," also known as "My Country 'Tis of Thee," is our national hymn. Whereas the former, written in a time of great national crisis, proudly celebrates our strength and eminence, "America," created in a more contemplative moment, gives humble thanks for the abundant blessings of both our land and our nation.

"America" was born during a time of national tranquility, when life was still simple and the changes and innovations that would revolutionize the country were just beginning. The song's author, the Reverend Samuel Smith of Amherst, Massachusetts, had no grand ambitions for his work. Asked in 1831 by the renowned music educator and hymn-writer Lowell Mason for a patriotic school song, Smith turned to the familiar tune of the British national anthem, "God Save the King," and wrote his new lyrics in a single sitting. The song debuted shortly thereafter at a children's Fourth of July celebration at the Park Street Church in Boston.

Listeners immediately embraced Reverend Smith's quiet song, and it remains a standard today. The peaceful strains of "America" touch all who appreciate the blessings of our land and our nation.

26

The bald eagle, the red, white, and blue of the flag, and the Statue of Liberty are symbols we all cherish. The same is true of Reverend Smith's simple song "America." As familiar to every American as the sight of Old Glory waving in the breeze, the quiet song expresses our common love of our homeland and thankfulness for its blessings.

E PLURIBUS UNUM

THE UNITED STATES of AMERICA.

AMERICA

My native country, thee,
Land of the noble free,
Thy name I love;
I love thy rocks and rills,
Thy woods and templed hills,
My heart with rapture thrills,
Like that above.

Let music swell the breeze,
And ring from all the trees
Sweet freedom's song;
Let mortal tongues awake;
Let all that breathe partake;
Let rocks their silence break,
The sound prolong.

Our fathers' God to Thee,
Author of liberty,
To Thee we sing;
Long may our land be bright;
With freedom's holy light,
Protect us by Thy might,
Great God, our King.

THE BATTLE HYMN OF THE REPUBLIC

WORDS BY JULIA WARD HOWE

MUSIC TRADITIONAL

It is said that when President Lincoln heard "The Battle Hymn of the Republic" for the first time, he wept openly. With the Civil War threatening the very foundation of the country, the song was a moving reminder that the task Lincoln and his nation faced was above both politics and economics. Not only must the Union be preserved, but the higher authority of God must also be served.

The song had come a long way from the coarse "John Brown's Body," a marching song sung to the same tune by Union soldiers. Julia Ward Howe, a Boston poet, heard the Union song and, inspired by the music and the tragic circumstances of the Civil War, wrote a new set of lyrics. Her stirring new song, "The Battle Hymn of the Republic," appeared in the *Atlantic Monthly* in February of 1862 and soon became the Union anthem.

But Howe's song was about unification in God's army, not division amongst the armies of men, and many in the South embraced the song as fully as their countrymen in the North. Howe herself wrote that her song was not about North or South but about "the sacredness of human liberty." With this timeless message, "The Battle Hymn of the Republic" survived the Civil War to provide inspiration at such diverse places as the political campaigns of Ulysses S. Grant and William Jennings Bryan, the funeral services for Winston Churchill, and the inauguration of President Jimmy Carter.

Although "The Battle Hymn of the Republic" has become universally popular, it will always be tied closely to the tragedy of the Civil War era. The same is true for President Abraham Lincoln, whose courage and integrity preserved the American union. This portrait by American artist J. L. G. Ferris depicts a passionate Lincoln speaking at Independence Hall in Philadelphia.

THE BATTLE HYMN OF THE REPUBLIC

Mine eyes have seen the glo-ry of the com-ing of the Lord: He is

tram-pling out the vin-tage where the grapes of wrath are stored; He hath

loosed the fate-ful light-ning of His ter-ri-ble swift sword: His truth is marching on.

Chorus

Glo-ry! Glo-ry! Hal-le-lu-jah! Glo-ry! Glo-ry! Glo-ry! Hal-le-lu-jah!

Glo-ry! Glo-ry! Hal-le-lu-jah! His truth is march-ing on.

I have seen Him in the watchfires
Of a hundred circling camps;
They have builded Him an altar
In the evening dews and damps;
I can read His righteous sentence
By the dim and flaring lamps;
His day is marching on.
Chorus

He has sounded forth the trumpet
That shall never sound retreat;
He is sifting out the hearts of men
Before His judgment seat;
O be swift, my soul, to answer Him;
Be jubilant my feet!
Our God is marching on.
Chorus

In the beauty of the lilies,
Christ was born across the sea,
With a glory in His bosom that
Transfigures you and me;
As He died to make men holy,
Let us live to make men free,
While God is marching on.
Chorus

He is coming like the glory
Of the morning on the wave;
He is wisdom to the mighty,
He is honor to the brave;
So the world shall be His footstool,
And the soul of wrong His slave,
Our God is marching on.
Chorus

THE BATTLE CRY OF FREEDOM

WORDS AND MUSIC BY GEORGE F. ROOT

Early in 1861, President Lincoln called for volunteers to join the fight to preserve the Union. George F. Root, a songwriter and musician living in Chicago, answered the call the only way he knew: with a song. The very day of Lincoln's call, Root wrote "The Battle Cry of Freedom." The popular singing duo of Frank and Jules Lombard performed the song soon thereafter in Chicago's Court House Square; in no time at all "The Battle Cry of Freedom" had swept though the northern states, reaching Union troops, who found comfort and inspiration in Root's moving song.

George Root composed two sets of lyrics for his song: a rallying song for the general public and a marching song for the troops. Not to be denied, the southern soldiers adapted the song to their own cause, writing their own lyrics to Root's moving tune.

So powerful and pervasive was the effect of "The Battle Cry of Freedom" on the troops that after the war President Lincoln gave George Root special praise, telling him he had "done more than a hundred generals and a thousand orators" to maintain the spirits of the American people. George F. Root, answering his nation's call for service, proved yet again the wonderful, inspirational power of song.

The city of Washington, D. C., is full of monuments to great Americans who have served their country and helped preserve and define the American way of life. But American monuments and celebrations also pay tribute to the individuals who serve their country in quiet ways, men like George F. Root, who answered his president's call with a song.

THE BATTLE CRY OF FREEDOM

Yes we'll ral - ly round the flag, boys, we'll ral - ly once a - gain,

Shout- ing the bat- tle- cry of Free - dom, We will ral - ly from the hill - side, we'll

Chorus

gath- er from the plain, Shout- ing the bat- tle- cry of Free - dom, The

Un- ion for- ev- er, Hur - rah boys, hur- rah! Down with the Trai- tor, Up with the Star; While we

ral- ly round the flag, boys, Ral- ly once a- gain, Shout- ing the bat- tle- cry of Free- dom.

36

We are springing to the call
Of our brothers gone before,
Shouting the battle cry of freedom;
And we'll fill the vacant ranks
With a million freemen more,
Shouting the battle cry of freedom.
Chorus

We will welcome to our numbers
The loyal, true and brave,
Shouting the battle cry of freedom;
And although he may be poor
He shall never be a slave,
Shouting the battle cry of freedom.
Chorus

So we're springing to the call
From the East and from the West,
Shouting the battle cry of freedom;
And we'll hurl the rebel crew
From the land we love the best,
Shouting the battle cry of freedom.
Chorus

37

When Johnny Comes Marching Home Again

WORDS AND MUSIC BY PATRICK SARSFIELD GILMORE

When Johnny Comes Marching Home Again," first published in Boston in 1863, touched on one of the most powerful emotions of the Civil War—one shared by the entire American nation, North and South alike. The melancholy, yet hopeful, song speaks of the safe return of soldiers, a goal that unified individual American families across geographical and political boundaries.

The song's author, Patrick Sarsfield Gilmore, was an Irish-born band leader who made his home in Boston. During the war he was stationed in New Orleans, working with military bands. Perhaps his unique, international perspective allowed him to see more clearly the feelings that united Americans rather than only the issues that divided them.

Gilmore's song was a sweeping success in his own day, and it has resurfaced throughout American history, whenever the pain and suffering of war have caused us to unite as a nation in support of our soldiers and the families they leave behind. The song serves as a reminder that we must never forget the human side of all political conflicts and that we must never lose compassion for those who make a willing sacrifice for our country.

Eastman Johnson's *The Wounded Drummer Boy* depicts the many sides of war: the bravery of those who serve, the camaraderie among fellow soldiers, and the tragedy of young lives given to battle. Like the song "When Johnny Comes Marching Home Again," Johnson's painting serves as a reminder of the terrible human cost of war.

WHEN JOHNNY COMES MARCHING HOME AGAIN

When John-ny comes march-ing home a-gain, Hur-rah! Hur-rah! We'll give him a heart-y wel-come then, Hur-rah! Hur-rah! The men will cheer the boys will shout, The lad-ies they will all turn out, And we'll all feel gay When John-ny comes march-ing home.

Get ready for the Jubilee,
Hurrah! Hurrah!
We'll give the hero three times three,
Hurrah! Hurrah!
The laurel wreath is ready now
To place upon his loyal brow,
And we'll all feel gay
When Johnny comes marching home.

In eighteen hundred and sixty-one,
Hurrah! Hurrah!
That was when the war begun,
Hurrah! Hurrah!
In eighteen hundred and sixty-two,
Both sides were falling to,
And we'll all feel gay
When Johnny comes marching home.

In eighteen hundred and sixty-three,
Hurrah! Hurrah!
Abe Lincoln did the slaves set free,
Hurrah! Hurrah!
In eighteen hundred and sixty-three
Abe Lincoln did the slaves set free
And we'll all feel gay
When Johnny comes marching home.

In eighteen hundred and sixty-four
Hurrah! Hurrah!
Abe called for five hundred thousand more,
Hurrah! Hurrah!
In eighteeen hundred and sixty-five
They talked rebellion and strife;
And we'll all feel gay
When Johnny comes marching home.

AMERICA THE BEAUTIFUL
WORDS BY KATHARINE LEE BATES
MUSIC BY SAMUEL AUGUSTUS WARD

As the United States expanded westward in the last half of the nineteenth century, Americans shared a growing sense of awe at the great natural gifts the frontier revealed. Katharine Lee Bates, an English professor at Wellesley College in Massachusetts, toured the West in the summer of 1893. Like most Americans accustomed to the landscape of the East, Bates felt overwhelmed by the vastness and the beauty of an America she had never before seen.

Standing atop Pike's Peak in Colorado that summer, Bates pondered the wonderful diversity of her nation's natural beauty. She returned to her hotel room and wrote the words we now know as "America the Beautiful." Bates did not immediately think of her poem as lyrics to a patriotic song; but in 1911, "America the Beautiful," paired with music by Samuel Augustus Ward, appeared in print.

Americans embraced the new song as an open expression of what each had felt in his own heart: that theirs was an especially blessed nation with natural gifts beyond compare. "America the Beautiful" gave voice to the gratitude and reverence that Americans felt in the days when the West was just beginning to reveal itself, and that we still feel today.

When Katharine Lee Bates gazed upon the splendor of the Rocky Mountains and wrote the verses to "America the Beautiful," she was looking at a landscape more vast and wonderful than she could have ever imagined. Her experience would be hard to recreate today, with television and fast, easy travel. Nonetheless, the awe and reverence that she felt are familiar to all Americans who pause to consider the great and varied natural beauty of their homeland.

AMERICA THE BEAUTIFUL

44

O beautiful for pilgrim feet,
Whose stern, impassioned stress
A thoroughfare for freedom beat
Across the wilderness!
America! America! God mend thine every flaw,
Confirm thy soul in self-control,
Thy liberty in law!

O beautiful for heroes proved
In liberating strife,
Who more than self their country loved,
And mercy more than life!
America! America! May God thy gold refine,
Till all success be nobleness,
And every grace divine!

O beautiful for patriot dream
That sees beyond the years
Thine alabaster cities gleam,
Undimmed by human tears!
America! America! God shed His grace on thee,
And crown thy good with brotherhood
From sea to shining sea!

THE STARS AND STRIPES FOREVER

WORDS AND MUSIC BY JOHN PHILIP SOUSA

Americans faced the approach of the twentieth century with a powerful national pride and an unwavering faith in the unlimited and unmatched possibilities of their nation. In the midst of this era of patriotism, John Philip Sousa, who had commanded the United States Marine Band, was returning home from a trip to Europe when he had a sudden inspiration. As he stood on the deck thinking of home, the notes of a new patriotic march sprang into his head, and with them a glorious vision of the American flag. Sousa recalled later: "I could see the stars and stripes flying from the flagstaff of the White House just as plainly as if I were back there again . . . and to my imagination it seemed to be the biggest, grandest flag in the world." Once on shore, Sousa enlarged his vision into the march we all know as "The Stars and Stripes Forever."

Sousa's new song became the most successful march ever written, its proud and confident strains capturing the spirit of Americans enraptured by the beauty, grandeur, and limitless possibilities of their county. Sousa's march possesses the power to inspire in us the same glorious visions of our flag and our nation that Sousa himself saw on the Atlantic headed toward American shores.

Born in 1854 to a trombone player in the United States Marine Band, John Philip Sousa grew up to become the musical director of his father's band—known as "The President's Own Band"— and one of the greatest names in American patriotic music. His stirring marches are timeless classics, as much a part of American patriotism as fireworks, flag waving, and the Fourth of July.

46

THE STARS AND STRIPES FOREVER

1. Let mar-tial note In tri-umph float, And lib-er-ty ex-tend its
2. Let ea-gle shriek From lof-ty peak, The nev-er-end-ing watch-word

might-y hand, A flag ap-pears, 'Mid thun-d'rous cheers, The ban-ner of the West-ern-
of our land. Let sum-mer breeze Waft through the trees The ech-o of the chor-us

land. The em-blem of the brave and true, Its folds pro-tect no
grand. Sing out for lib-er-ty and light, Sing out for free-dom

ty - rant crew, The red and white and star-ry blue, Is Free-dom's shield and
and the right, Sing out for Un-ion and its might, Oh, pa-tri-ot-ic

hope. Oth-er na-tions may deem their flags the
Sons!

47

48

The — Ban - ner of the Right.— — Let

des - pots re - mem - ber the day— — When our

fa - thers with might - ty en - deav - or, Pro -

claim'd as they march'd to the fray,— — That by their

might, And by their right, It waves for - ev - er!

49

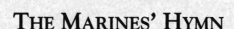

THE MARINES' HYMN

MUSIC BY JACQUES OFFENBACH
WORDS BY UNKNOWN COMPOSER

The Colors of the United States Marine Corps are inscribed with the phrase "From the shores of Tripoli to the Halls of the Montezumas." These same words, transposed for the sake of rhyme, open "The Marines' Hymn," a rousing march which pays tribute to the Corps' glorious past and pledges continued service across the globe.

The music for the hymn comes from a Jacques Offenbach opera, popular in France in the mid-nineteenth century. How the French tune came to serve as the music for the United States Marine hymn is as uncertain as the origin of the song's lyrics, which seem to have evolved through the years, with a verse being added for each new challenge taken on by the Corps. The Marines established three official verses in 1929, words which solemnly promise the valiant service of the U.S. Marine Corps in any corner of the globe, in any battle, and at any time that right and freedom need protection.

50

THE MARINES' HYMN

51

ANCHORS AWEIGH

WORDS BY ALFRED HART, ROYAL LOVELL, AND GEORGE D. LOTTMAN
MUSIC BY CHARLES ZIMMERMAN

Up until 1906, tradition at the United States Naval Academy demanded that a new march be composed for each graduating class. That tradition disappeared, however, with the composition of "Anchors Aweigh." Written by Naval Academy Band leader Charles Zimmerman for the class of 1907, "Anchors Aweigh" was immediately embraced as the unofficial anthem of the U.S. Navy.

The song debuted in 1906 at the traditional Army-Navy football game. Fittingly, the first lyrics were those of a rousing fight song, depicting the exploits of the Navy on the football field rather than on the oceans of the world. But the song was so popular that some years later new lyrics were added to pay tribute to the more solemn tasks of the Navy. It is these words that are today sung at parades and ceremonies honoring the proud and brave men and women of the United States Navy.

53

The United States Marine Corps War Memorial pays tribute to the courageous service of the United States Marines. Created in 1954 by Felix W. deWeldon, the sculpture is a recreation of a photograph taken at Iwo Jima in February of 1945. The inscription on the sculpture reads: "In honor and memory of the men of the United States Marine Corps who have given their lives for their country since November 11, 1775."

54

This Thomas Birch painting, part of the art collection of the United States Naval Academy, depicts the battle between the great ships USS *Constitution* and the British HMS *Guerriere* on August 19, 1812. Since the beginning of our nation, the U.S. Navy has proudly and bravely fought on the oceans of the world.

ANCHORS AWEIGH

An - chors A - weigh my boys, An - chors A - weigh
Stand Na - vy down the field, Sail set to the sky!

Fare - well to col - lege joys, we sail at break of
We'll nev - er change our course so, Ar - my you steer

day— day— day— day! Through our last night on shore,
shy— y— y— y Roll up the score Na - vy

Drink to the foam, Un - til we
An - chors A - weigh Sail Na - vy

meet once more Here's wish - ing you a hap - py voy - age home.
down the field And sink the Ar - my, sink the Ar - my gray.

THE CAISSONS GO ROLLING ALONG

O-ver hill, o-ver dale, As we hit the dust-y trail, And the Cais-sons go rol-ling a-long._ In and out, hear them shout coun-ter march and right a-bout, And the Cais-sions go roll-ing a-long._ Then it's hi! hi! hee! in the field ar-til-ler-y, Shout out your num-bers loud and strong,_ For where-e'er you go, You will al-ways know That the Cais-sions go roll-ing a-long._

56

The United States Military Academy Color Guard proud-ly carries the colors of their country, their service, and their academy. Behind the Color Guard are the buildings at West Point and the statue of our first president, George Washington.

THE CAISSONS GO ROLLING ALONG

WORDS AND MUSIC BY BRIGADIER GENERAL EDMUND L. GRUBER

The proud verses of "The Caissons Go Rolling Along" were inspired by the rather mundane sight of field artillery soldiers slowly moving ammunition boxes, or caissons, across the rugged Sambales Mountains in the Phillippines in 1908. Lt. Edmund L. Gruber paid tribute to the hard work of these soldiers with "The Caissons Go Rolling Along," which soon thereafter became the official song of the Fifth Field Artillery.

Lieutenant Gruber went on to become a brigadier general, and his song became a permanent part of army life. Today, "The Caissons Go Rolling Along" is not the official song of the United States Army, but it is the song that both the men and women of the army and Americans everywhere recognize as the anthem of their soldiers.

Trucks have replaced caissons, and the life of members of the field artillery and all soldiers has changed drastically since the days of Lieutenant Gruber, but one fact has remained unchanged. When the most difficult and least glamorous work of preserving the peace beckons, the men and women of the United States Army stand ready for service, with "The Caissons Go Rolling Along" to boost their spirits.

SEMPER PARATUS

WORDS AND MUSIC BY CAPTAIN FRANCIS S. VAN BOSKERK

Shortly before his death in 1927, Captain Francis S. Van Boskerk of the United States Coast Guard entrusted the editor of *The Coast Guard* magazine with the words and music to a song he called "Semper Paratus." It was the Captain's dream that this song would become the anthem of the Coast Guard. The editor did not betray Van Boskerk's trust. He published "Semper Paratus" with his full endorsement, and before long, Van Boskerk's beloved Coast Guard adopted his song as its anthem.

Captain Van Boskerk had no musical training. After writing the lyrics to his song he worked out a rough tune with the help of a violin-playing Coast Guard dentist. Before the song appeared in print it had been rearranged and completed by William Sima of the Naval Academy band. But Van Boskerk's lyrics needed no improvement. "Semper Paratus" translates in English as "always ready." To Van Boskerk, that was the proud motto of the Guard, a group of brave Americans ready to serve in any crisis.

SEMPER PARATUS

We're al - ways read - y for the call,_____ We place our trust in
We're al - ways read - y for the call,_____ We place our trust in

thee._____ Through surf and storm and howl - ing gale, High
thee;_____ Through howl - ing gale and shot and shell, To

shall our pur - pose be._____ "Sem-per Pa - ra-tus" is our
win our vic - to - ry._____ "Sem-per Pa - ra-tus" is our

guide,_____ Our fame, our glo - ry too,_____ To fight to
guide,_____ Our pledge, our mot - to too,_____ We're "Al - ways

save or fight and die! Aye! Coast Guard we are for you!_____
Read- y," do or die! Aye! Coast Guard we fight for you!_____

60

This beautiful tall ship is the Coast Guard training ship
Eagle. Originally part of the German training fleet, the
ship was captured by the American navy in World War II
and turned over to the Coast Guard as a training ship.
Today, Coast Guard cadets serve a term aboard the *Eagle*,
learning some of the sailing skills they will put to use in
defense of their country.

LORD, GUARD AND GUIDE THE MEN WHO FLY

Lord, guard and guide the men who fly, Through the great
Thou who dost keep with ten - der might The bal - anced
Con - trol their minds with in - stinct fit What time, ad -
A - loft in sol - i - tudes of space, Up - hold them

spa - ces of the sky; Be with them trav - ers -
birds in all their flight, Thou of the tem - pered
ven - tur - ing, they quit the firm se - cur - i -
with Thy sav - ing grace. O God, pro - tect the

62

ing the air In dark-ening storms or sun - shine fair.
winds be near, That, hav - ing Thee, they know no fear.
ty of land; Grant stead-fast eye and skill - ful hand.
men who fly Thru lone - ly ways be - neath the sky.

The Air Force Thunderbirds, F-16 jets used at air shows to
educate the public about the Air Force, are a symbol of the
power of the Force and its mastery of the skies.

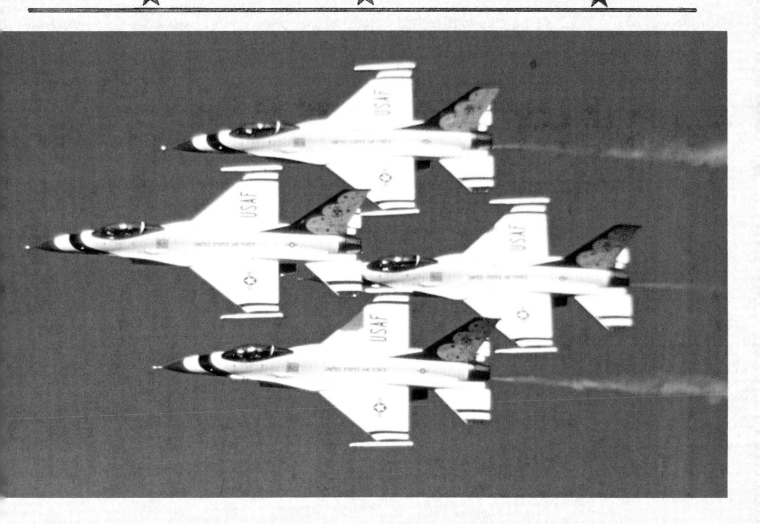

LORD, GUARD AND GUIDE THE MEN WHO FLY

WORDS BY MARY C. D. HAMILTON
MUSIC BY HENRY BAKER

Lord, Guard and Guide the Men Who Fly" is the Air Force's hymn for religious and solemn occasions. The hymn humbly asks for the hand of God to lead and protect the men and women of the Air Force as they proudly serve their nation.

Mary C. D. Hamilton's hymn is a fine balance to military songs which proclaim the bravery of the men and women of the armed forces, for it acknowledges not only the danger of their tasks and the courage of their service, but their ultimate dependence upon God for strength and protection.

THE 4TH OF JULY.

YANKEE DOODLE BOY

WORDS AND MUSIC BY GEORGE M. COHAN

Although George M. Cohan wrote "Yankee Doodle Boy" more than a century after the American colonists boldly claimed the original British "Yankee Doodle" as their own, he wrote and sang his song with the same spirit of patriotic rebellion that inspired his forefathers.

Cohan, the son of two vaudevillians and a performer from the age of nine, was a revolutionary in his own right, creating a new, distinctly American genre of theatre—the musical comedy—when so many contemporaries were simply imitating European forms.

Starring in *Little Johnny Jones* on the broadway stage between 1904 and 1907, Cohan sang "Yankee Doodle Boy" as the lead character, a young American jockey gone to England to ride in the Derby. There was a great deal of George M. Cohan in both the character of Johnny Jones and the featured song. Cohan was a man intensely proud of his American heritage—proud of his American accent, his American music, and his American ideals. When he sang "Yankee Doodle Boy" his listeners couldn't help but feel the same way. The music of George M. Cohan gave Americans the opportunity to express their unabashed patriotism.

65

Like this charming antique postcard depicting two small children waving the Stars and Stripes, the music of George M. Cohan appeals to the patriot in every American. His spirited patriotic songs have made Cohan a true American hero. Despite the fact that he was born on the third—not the fourth—of July, no American can dispute Cohan's self-proclaimed title of the one and only "Yankee Doodle Boy."

YANKEE DOODLE BOY

I'm a Yan - kee Doo - dle Dan -

dy, A Yan - kee Doo - dle, do or

die; _____ A real live

nep - hew of my Un - cle Sam's,

Born on the Fourth of Ju - ly. _____

66

I've got a Yan - kee Doo - dle sweet - heart, She's my Yan - kee Doo - dle joy.

Yan - kee Doo - dle came to Lon - don, Just to ride the pon - ies; I am the Yan - kee Doo - dle Boy.

67

You're a Grand Old Flag

WORDS AND MUSIC BY GEORGE M. COHAN

The flag is the greatest and most powerful of American symbols. George M. Cohan experienced this power in 1910 while riding in a funeral procession with an elderly Civil War veteran. The old man, after recalling for Cohan Pickett's charge at Gettysburg, embraced the folded American flag he held in his lap and told the performer he did it all for her, for "she's a grand old rag."

So taken with the old man's phrase was Cohan that he immediately turned it into a song. And so taken was he with his own song that he wrote an entire play around it. *George Washington, Jr.*, became one of the most successful musical comedies of the day. It featured Cohan in the role of a patriotic young man so proud of his country that he adopts the name of its legendary first president. The highlight of each performance was Cohan's song "You're a Grand Old Flag" ("rag" had been changed to "flag" after charges of disrespect). Strutting across the stage draped in the stars and stripes, Cohan delivered the song with the patriotic pride that was his trademark.

"You're a Grand Old Flag" became an American classic. Cohan's irrepressible patriotic spirit and the emotional appeal of our flag were a combination that patriotic Americans found impossible to resist.

68

Betsy Griscom Ross, 1752-1836, is credited as the maker of the first American flag. This painting, *Betsy Ross Shows George Washington the Stars and Stripes*, by Edward Percy Moran, depicts Ross displaying her handiwork for the new nation's first president. Today, with an increase to fifty stars, Old Glory remains our nation's most cherished emblem.

YOU'RE A GRAND OLD FLAG

You're a grand old flag you're a high fly - ing flag, And for - ev - er in peace may you wave. You're the em - blem of the land I love, The home of the free and the

brave._____ Ev - 'ry heart beats

true un - der Red, White and Blue, Where there's

nev - er a boast or brag;_____ "But should

auld ac - quain - tance be for - got," Keep your

eye on the grand old flag._____

OVER THERE

WORDS AND MUSIC BY GEORGE M. COHAN

George M. Cohan once called "Over There" the "dramatization of a bugle call." No description could be more apt. Written on April 7, 1917, the day after President Wilson signed the declaration propelling the United States into World War I, Cohan's rousing song summoned Americans to the service of their nation.

Cohan's song reflected American pride and confidence as the nation entered into an international conflict, ready to fight in order to make a difference in the world. But it also served to bolster courage and lift morale on the battle lines and on the home front when the harsh realities of war began to hit home.

By the end of the war over two million copies of the sheet music for "Over There" were in circulation. President Wilson praised the song as "a genuine inspiration to all American manhood." An even greater tribute came a quarter of a century later, when George M. Cohan received the Congressional Medal of Honor in recognition of the contribution he had made to his country in a time of great crisis with the rallying words and music of "Over There" and other songs. This was the first time in history that the government had officially recognized the undeniable power of song to inspire and comfort the American people.

72

Howard Chandler Christy, born in 1873 in Ohio, was one of several American artists whose work appeared on World War I recruiting posters. The posters called upon an eager public to join in America's first international war effort. Christy also painted a mural, *The Signing of the Constitution,* which graces the walls of the Rotunda of the Capitol in Washington.

OVER THERE

So pre - pare, _____ say a pray'r, _____

Send the word, send the word to be - ware, _____

We'll be o - ver, we're com - ing o -

ver, And we won't come back till it's

1. o - ver o - ver there. **2.** O - ver there.

75

THIS LAND IS YOUR LAND
WORDS AND MUSIC BY WOODY GUTHRIE

Woody Guthrie, the author of the American folk classic "This Land Is Your Land," was born in 1912 in Oklahoma. His childhood and youth were poor and troubled, and at a very young age he found himself alone, travelling to California after the devastation of the Oklahoma Dust Bowl. Guthrie eventually found success as a folk singer and songwriter, but he did not forget the hard life of the common people he had known as a child and a young man. It was for these people that he wrote "This Land Is Your Land."

Written in 1940, Guthrie's song told listeners that the country belonged to each and every one of them, and that all Americans shared a responsibility to make their country the best it could be. Guthrie wrote "This Land Is Your Land" as a reminder that the beauty and blessings of America should be shared equally by all Americans. Today, Guthrie's simple song about freedom and equality, which has been recorded by artists from Peter, Paul, and Mary to the Mormon Tabernacle Choir and is known by every American school child, ranks among the best-known and best-loved American patriotic folk songs of all time.

Woody Guthrie's patriotism was simple to understand. He loved the American land and he loved the American people. His song evokes images like this one of the Oregon coast, a scene which reminds all Americans of the source of their pride and patriotism.

THIS LAND IS YOUR LAND

This land is your land,—— This land is my land,—

— from Cal - i - for - nia —— to the New York

is - land;—— From the red - wood for - est ——

— to the Gulf Stream wa - ters ———

This land was made for you and me.

78

As I was walking that ribbon of highway,
I saw above me that endless skyway:
I saw below me that golden valley:
This land was made for you and me.

I've roamed and rambled and I followed my footsteps
To the sparkling sands of her diamond deserts;
And all around me a voice was sounding:
This land was made for you and me.

When the sun came shining, and I was strolling,
And the wheat fields waving and the dust clouds rolling,
As the fog was lifting a voice was chanting:
This land was made for you and me.

INDEX

80

A   1
B   2
C   3
D   4
E   5
F   6
G   7
H   8
I   9
J   0